Stories retold by Gaby Goldsack
Illustrated by Kim Blundell, Ruth Galloway and Emma Lake

Language consultant: Betty Root

This edition published by Parragon in 2011

Parragon
Queen Street House
4 Queen Street
Bath BA1 1HE, UK

ISBN 978-1-4454-4159-7

Printed in China

Please retain this information for future reference.

Classic
Read-Along
Collection

Bath • New York • Singapore • Hong Kong • Cologne • Delhi
Melbourne • Amsterdam • Johannesburg • Auckland • Shenzhen

Helping Your Child to Read

Learning to read is an exciting challenge for most children. From a very early age, sharing story books with children, talking about the pictures and guessing what might happen next are all very important parts of the reading experience.

Sharing reading

Set aside a regular quiet time to share reading with younger children, or to be on hand to encourage older children as they develop into independent readers.

The stories in this treasury are intended to encourage and support the early stages of learning to read. They present well-loved tales that children will happily listen to again and again. Familiarity helps children to identify some of the words and phrases.

When you feel your child is ready to move on a little, encourage them to join in so that you read the story aloud together. Always pause to talk about the pictures. The easy-to-read speech bubbles provide an excellent 'joining-in' activity. The bright, clear illustrations and matching text will help children to understand each story.

Building confidence

In time, children will want to read to you. When this happens, be patient and give continual praise. They may not read all the words correctly, but children's substitutions are often very good guesses. The repetition in each story is particularly helpful for building confidence. If your child cannot read a particular word, go back to the beginning of the sentence and read it together so the meaning is not lost. Most importantly, do not continue if your child is tired or simply in need of a change.

Reading alone

The next step is for your child to read alone. Try to be on hand to give help and support. Remember to give lots of encouragement and praise.

The collection of stories in **My Read-Along Treasury** will help children to find reading an enjoyable and rewarding experience.

Contents

Goldilocks and the Three Bears

Once upon a time there were three bears. They lived in a little house in a big wood.

There was great big Daddy Bear.

I'm big.

Then there
was middle-sized
Mummy Bear.

I'm middle
sized.

I'm just
little.

And there was
tiny little
Baby Bear.

One day, Mummy Bear made porridge.
She put some in a great big bowl.

She put some in a middle-sized bowl.
And she put some in a tiny little bowl.

The porridge was too hot to eat.
The three bears went for a walk
while it cooled down.

Not far away, a little girl was also walking in the big wood. The little girl had golden hair. She was called Goldilocks.

Is anyone home?

Soon Goldilocks found the house of the three bears. The door was wide open.

Goldilocks walked right into the house.
She saw the bowls of porridge. She
tasted some from the great big bowl.
It was too salty.

She tasted some from the middle-sized bowl.
It was too sweet.

She tasted some from the tiny little bowl.
It was just right. Goldilocks ate it all up!

Then Goldilocks saw three chairs.
She sat in the great big chair.
It was too high.

She sat in the middle-sized chair.
It was too low.

She sat in the tiny little chair.
It was just right.

Crack! Oh no, it wasn't! Goldilocks
was too heavy. The tiny little chair
broke into pieces.

Next Goldilocks went upstairs.

She lay on the great big bed. It was too hard.

She lay on the middle-sized bed. It was too soft.

She lay on the tiny little bed. It was just right, and Goldilocks fell asleep.

Soon the three bears came home.

"Who's been eating my porridge?"
asked Daddy Bear in a great big voice.

"Who's been eating my porridge?" asked
Mummy Bear in a middle-sized voice.

22

"Who's been eating my porridge, and eaten it all up?" asked Baby Bear in a tiny little voice.

Then the three bears saw their chairs.
"Who's been sitting in my chair?" asked
Daddy Bear in a great big voice.

"Who's been sitting in my chair?" asked
Mummy Bear in a middle-sized voice.

"Who's been sitting in my chair and broken it?" asked Baby Bear in a tiny little voice.

Then the three bears went upstairs.
"Who's been sleeping in my bed?" asked
Daddy Bear in a great big voice.

"Who's been sleeping in my bed?" asked
Mummy Bear in a middle-sized voice.

"Who's been sleeping in my bed?"
asked Baby Bear in a tiny little voice.
"And she's still here!"

Just then, Goldilocks woke up. When she
saw the three bears, she was scared.

Goldilocks jumped up and rushed down the
stairs. Then she ran out of the house.

The three bears did not see Goldilocks
ever again.

How many of these words can you read?
The pictures will help you. Look back in your book
and see if you can find the words in the story.

Baby Bear   Daddy Bear   Mummy Bear

Goldilocks   wood   house

chair   bed   bowl   door

The Emperor's New Clothes

Once upon a time there was an Emperor who loved clothes. He spent all his money on new clothes. He would change five or six times a day.

One day, two clever thieves came to see the Emperor. They told the Emperor that they were weavers.

"We can weave beautiful cloth," said one thief.

"And it is magic," said the other.
"Only clever people can see the cloth. Stupid people see nothing."

"Make me a suit from this magic cloth,"
said the Emperor. "Then I will be able
to tell who is clever and who is stupid."

"We will need lots of gold thread," said the first thief.

So the Emperor gave them lots of gold thread.

The thieves put the gold thread into their bags. Then they pretended to weave the cloth but they did not use the gold thread.

Really they were doing nothing at all.

The next day, the Emperor sent his Prime Minister to see the cloth.

The Prime Minister looked and looked. He could not see anything.

"I must be stupid," he thought.
"The Emperor must not find out."

He told the Emperor that it was the best cloth he had ever seen.

The next day, the two thieves went
to see the Emperor.

"We need more gold thread to make your suit," said the first thief.
"You shall have all the thread you need," said the Emperor.

The two thieves pretended to make the cloth into a suit.

The Emperor went to see the suit. He looked and looked. He could not see anything.

"I must be stupid," he thought. "No one must find out."

"It is beautiful!" he cried.

The Emperor was very pleased.
He spoke to the Prime Minister.
"We must have a parade. Everyone
will be able to see my new suit."

46

The two thieves pretended to work
all day and all night.

At last the suit was ready.

The Emperor came to try on his new suit.

"It will feel lovely. It will feel as if you are wearing nothing," said the first thief.

48

They pretended to dress the Emperor in his new suit.

The Emperor and his Prime Minister looked and looked, but they could not see anything.

The Emperor led the parade in his new suit.
Everyone looked and looked, but they could
not see the new suit.

Then one little girl started to laugh.
"The Emperor has no clothes on," she cried.

And soon everyone, even the Emperor, saw that she was right.

"Oh no!" said the Emperor. "I have been very stupid."

And the thieves were never seen again.

How many of these words can you read?
The pictures will help you. Look back in your book
and see if you can find the words in the story.

Emperor

clothes

gold thread

thieves

money

parade

Prime Minister

little girl

The Three Billy Goats Gruff

Once upon a time there were three Billy Goats Gruff.

There was a big Billy Goat Gruff.

There was a middle-sized Billy Goat Gruff.

And there was a little Billy Goat Gruff.

The three goats all loved to eat grass.
They ate grass all day long on the hill.
But they never crossed the bridge to eat
the grass on the other side.

They never crossed the bridge because
the Troll lived under the bridge.

The Troll was very bad. He ate anyone
who dared to cross his bridge.

One day the little Billy Goat Gruff
looked at the green, green grass
on the other side of the bridge.

"I'm not scared of a silly old Troll," he said. "I'm going to cross the bridge."

"Me too," said the middle-sized Billy Goat Gruff.

"And me," said the big Billy Goat Gruff.

"You go first. It was your idea," said the big
Billy Goat Gruff to the little Billy Goat Gruff.

Trip, trap, trip, trip, trap!

So the little Billy Goat Gruff set off across the bridge.

Trip, trap, trip, trip, trap went his hooves.

"Who is that trip-trapping over my bridge?" roared the Troll.

"It's only me!" said the little Billy Goat Gruff. "I'm going to eat the green, green grass on the other side of the bridge."

"Oh no, you're not!" roared the Troll. "I'm going to eat you up!"

"But I am just little," said the little Billy Goat Gruff. "Wait until my middle-sized brother comes across. He is far bigger than me."

"Very well!" said the Troll.

Very well!

So the little Billy Goat Gruff crossed the bridge. Soon he was eating the green, green grass.

Next, the middle-sized Billy Goat Gruff crossed the bridge.

Who goes there?

"Who is that trip-trapping over my bridge?" roared the Troll.

"It's only me!" said the middle-sized Billy Goat Gruff. "I am going to eat the green, green grass on the other side of the bridge."

"Oh no, you're not!" roared the Troll. "I'm going to eat you up!"

I'm going to eat you up!

"But I am just middle-sized," said the middle-sized Billy Goat Gruff. "Wait until my big brother comes across. He is far bigger than me."

"Very well!" said the Troll.

And don't come back!

So the middle-sized Billy Goat Gruff crossed the bridge. Soon he was eating the green, green grass.

Next the big Billy Goat Gruff crossed the bridge.

Quake! Shake! Rumble!

"Who is that trip-trapping over my bridge?" roared the Troll.

"It's only me!" said the big Billy Goat Gruff. "I'm going to eat the green, green grass on the other side of the bridge."

"Oh no, you're not!" roared the Troll. "I'm going to eat you up!"

I'm going to eat you up!

The Troll jumped onto the bridge.

The big Billy Goat Gruff lowered his horns and charged.

Crash! The big Billy Goat Gruff banged into the Troll. The Troll flew into the air. Splash! He fell into the water.

Take that!

Crash!

Splash!

The big Billy Goat Gruff skipped over the bridge. Soon he was eating the green, green grass.

And the ugly Troll was never seen again.

Hooray!

How many of these words can you read?
The pictures will help you. Look back in your book
and see if you can find the words in the story.

big goat

bridge

little goat

grass

middle-sized goat

horns

hooves

hill

Troll

Little Red Riding Hood

Once upon a time there was a little girl. She wore a red hood and cloak. Everyone called her Little Red Riding Hood.

One day Little Red Riding Hood's mother said,

"Granny is ill. Take her this basket of food."

Little Red Riding Hood's granny lived on the other side of the wood.

I'm going to Granny's house!

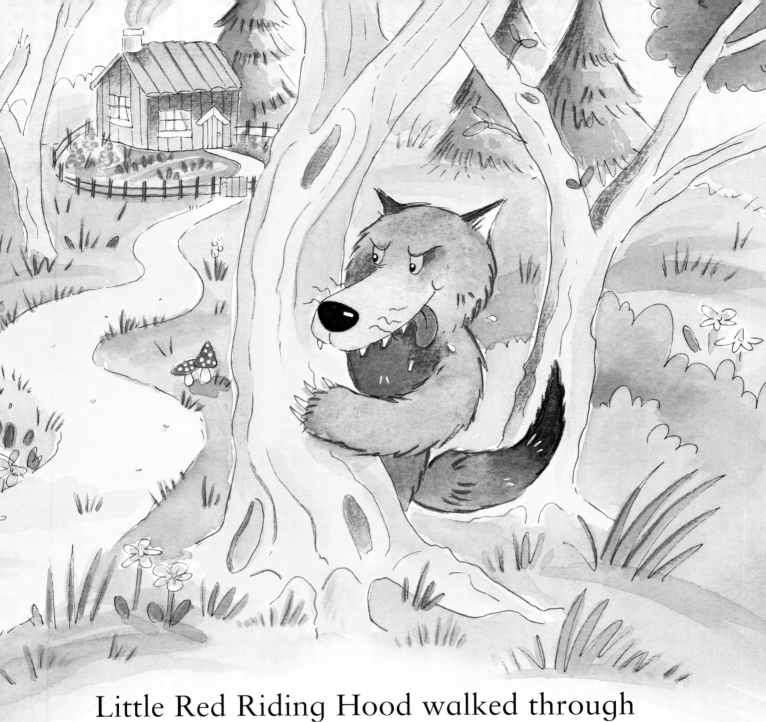

Little Red Riding Hood walked through the wood towards her granny's house.

She did not see a hungry wolf watching her.

The hungry wolf jumped out in front of Little Red Riding Hood.

"Where are you going?" he asked.

"I'm taking this basket of food to Granny who is ill," said Little Red Riding Hood.

To Granny's house.

"Where does your granny live?" asked the wolf.

"She lives in a house on the other side of the wood," said Little Red Riding Hood.

The hungry wolf smiled.

Why don't you pick some flowers?

"Why don't you pick flowers for your granny?" he said.

"What a good idea," said Little Red Riding Hood.

Little Red Riding Hood put down her basket to pick some flowers.

The hungry wolf smiled.

Then he ran off to Granny's house.

When he got there, the hungry wolf ate Granny in one big gulp.

But he was still hungry!

The hungry wolf put on Granny's cap and glasses. Then he got into Granny's bed and waited for Little Red Riding Hood.

He did not have to wait long.
Little Red Riding Hood walked in.

"Hello, Granny," said Little Red Riding
Hood. Then she stopped and looked.

"Granny, what big eyes you have!"
said Little Red Riding Hood.

"All the better to see you with," said the hungry wolf.

"Granny, what big ears you have!" said Little Red Riding Hood.

"All the better to hear you with," said the hungry wolf.

"Granny, what big teeth you have!" said Little Red Riding Hood.

"All the better to eat you with," said the hungry wolf.

Little Red Riding Hood screamed.

Suddenly, the hungry wolf jumped out
of the bed and...

...ate Little Red Riding Hood in one big gulp!

Now the wolf was not hungry any more. He was very full. He lay on Granny's bed and fell asleep.

In the wood, a woodcutter heard Little Red Riding Hood scream.

He ran into the house. He saw the wolf asleep on Granny's bed and...

...killed it with his axe!

"Let us out!" cried Little Red Riding Hood
and Granny from inside the
wolf's tummy.

Stay for tea!

The woodcutter cut open the wolf's tummy. Out jumped Little Red Riding Hood and Granny.

Granny was so pleased to be saved that she invited the woodcutter to tea!

How many of these words can you read?
The pictures will help you. Look back in your book
and see if you can find the words in the story.

wolf

basket

bed

ears

eyes

flowers

Granny

axe

glasses

The Elves and the Shoemaker

Once upon a time there was a shoemaker and his wife. The shoemaker worked very hard. But they were very poor.

One day, all the shoemaker had left was one small piece of leather.

"I will only be able to make one pair of shoes," said the shoemaker.

The shoemaker cut out a pair of shoes.
He left them on his workbench to sew
the next morning.

The next morning, the shoemaker was surprised. He found a pair of shoes on his workbench.

They were perfect. But the shoemaker did not know who had sewn them.

That day, a rich lady came into the shop and put on the shoes.

"They are a perfect fit," said the rich lady. She gave the shoemaker a big bag of money.

Now the shoemaker had money to
buy leather for two pairs of shoes.

The shoemaker cut out two pairs of shoes.
He left them on his workbench to sew the
next morning.

The next morning, the shoemaker was surprised. He found two pairs of shoes on his workbench.

"They are perfect!" said his wife.

That day, a rich man came into the shop. He bought both pairs of shoes.

He gave the shoemaker two big bags of money.

The shoemaker was very happy.

Now he had enough money to buy leather to make four pairs of shoes.

Night after night, the same thing happened.

The shoemaker cut out the leather and left it on the workbench. Every morning he found perfect shoes in its place.

But the shoemaker still did not know
who was sewing the shoes.

One night, the shoemaker and his wife hid in the workshop.

They waited to see who would come.

At midnight, two tiny elves ran in. Their clothes were very old.

They jumped onto the workbench and started to sew. They did not stop until the last shoe was made.

"We must make the elves a present," said the shoemaker to his wife.

So the shoemaker made two pairs of tiny shoes. His wife made two tiny suits.

It took them a very long time.

One night, they left the shoes and suits on the workbench. Then they hid and waited to see what would happen.

At midnight, the two tiny elves ran in. They jumped up onto the workbench. They were surprised to see the tiny clothes and shoes.

They put on their new clothes and shoes.
They were very happy.

They liked the clothes and shoes.

The shoemaker and his wife never saw the elves again. But they did not mind. The elves had brought them good luck.

From that day on, the shoemaker worked harder than ever.

And they were never poor again.

How many of these words can you read?
The pictures will help you. Look back in your book
and see if you can find the words in the story.

elves

shoemaker

clothes

money

rich man

rich lady

wife

shoes

Cinderella

Once upon a time, there was a pretty girl called Cinderella. She lived with her stepmother and two ugly stepsisters. The ugly stepsisters did not like Cinderella. They made Cinderella do all the work.

One day, a card came from the Prince. There was to be a ball. Every girl in the land could go. But the stepsisters did not want Cinderella to go.

The stepsisters told Cinderella she could not go to the ball. She only had rags to wear. Cinderella was very sad.

Cinderella helped her sisters to get ready for the ball.

She helped them dress.

Help me dress, Cinderella!

She brushed their hair.
She tried very hard to
make them look pretty.
But it was no good.
They were just too
ugly.

The stepsisters went to the ball.
Cinderella was very sad.
She wanted to see the prince.
She sat by the fire and cried.

"Don't cry," said a voice.

It was Cinderella's fairy godmother. "You will go to the ball," said the fairy godmother.

You will go to the ball!

"Go and get a pumpkin," said the
fairy godmother.
Cinderella got the pumpkin.

"Go and get six white
mice," said the fairy
godmother.
Cinderella got
six white mice.

"Go and get two rats," said the
fairy godmother.
Cinderella got two rats.
"Go and get a frog," said the
fairy godmother.
Cinderella got a frog.

Ribbit!

The fairy godmother waved her
magic wand.
The pumpkin turned into a coach.
The mice turned into horses.
The two rats turned into footmen.
The frog turned into a driver.

It's magic!

The fairy godmother waved her
magic wand again.
Cinderella's dress turned into a
pretty ball gown.

Cinderella got into the coach.
"Be home before the clock strikes
midnight," said the fairy godmother.
"The magic ends at midnight."

Please dance with me!

At the ball, Cinderella saw the prince.
"Please dance with me," said the prince.
They danced all evening. The ugly sisters
did not know that the pretty girl
was Cinderella.

The clock struck midnight.
Cinderella said, "I must go home!"
"Come back!" said the prince.

Bong!
Bong!

Come back!

But Cinderella ran away.

She lost her shoe.

The prince picked it up.

The coach turned back into a pumpkin.

Cinderella's pretty ball gown turned back into rags.

Cinderella ran all the way home.

The next day,
the prince looked
for Cinderella.
Every girl in the land
tried on the lost shoe.
It would not fit.

Cinderella's stepsisters tried on the shoe.
It would not fit.

At last, Cinderella tried on the shoe.

It did fit!

"Will you marry me?" said the prince.

"Yes!" said Cinderella.

And so they were married and lived happily ever after.

How many of these words can you read?
The pictures will help you. Look back in your book
and see if you can find the words in the story.

clock   coach   fairy
godmother   frog

prince   gown   stepsisters

pumpkin   footman   mice

The end